you and me

Alone at home
The birthday party
The bullies
Gita gets lost

First published in hardback 1996 by
A & C Black (Publishers) Ltd
35 Bedford Row, London WC1R 4JH

Text copyright © Althea Braithwaite 1996
Illustrations copyright © Karin Littlewood 1996

ISBN 0-7136-4401-X

A CIP catalogue record for this book
is available from theBritish Library.

Typeset in New Century Schoolbook
Printed and bound in Italy by L.E.G.O. SPA

you and me

Gita gets lost

Althea

Illustrated by Karin Littlewood

A & C Black · London

Gita and her mum had
gone to the holiday market.
There was a big crowd
and it was very noisy.

Mum said, 'Hold on to my bag,
I don't want you getting
lost in this crowd.'

3

They stopped to watch a man
trying to sell china. He was throwing
it in the air and catching it again.

Gita almost hoped he would
drop something!

Mum wanted to buy some cheese.
Gita saw some shiny bangles
on another stall.

She let go of Mum's bag.
'I will just have a quick look,
while Mum buys the cheese.'

Gita saw a bangle she really liked.
She turned to find her mum.
She was going to ask if
she could have next week's pocket money.

But Mum was nowhere
to be seen.

All she could see
was coats and legs.
But where was her mum?
Gita pushed through the crowd.

Where had she gone?
She felt very scared.

'What am I going to do?'
What was it her mum had
told her to do
if she got lost?
'What is my name?'
She had forgotten.

She knew it was Gita,
but what came next?
'Oh yes, Gita Patel.'
She felt like crying.

13

Someone put a hand
on her shoulder,
but it wasn't her mum.
Gita felt frightened.
'Are you lost?
What's your name?'

Should she tell him?
Perhaps he was one of
those nasty people
who took children away.

Then she heard another person saying,
'Come on, love, we want to help you.'

'What's your mum wearing?
Can you remember?'
She couldn't.

They stood her on a stool
beside the fruit stall.
People crowded round her.
'Have you seen her mum?'
'Should we call the police?'
'Do you know where you live?'

Gita started crying.
Perhaps she would never
see her mum again.

'Here, have an apple,
that will cheer you up.'

Gita shook her head.
She knew she shouldn't take
food from strangers.
She couldn't eat anyway.
She felt sick.

Suddenly Mum pushed
her way through the crowd.
She was crying.

She was very angry.
'I told you to stay with me,
and to hold on to my bag.'

Then she hugged her and said,
'I was so frightened,
I didn't know where
you had gone.
Never, never do that again.'
Gita knew she wouldn't.

These are some of the things children said after reading the story:

"Why was the man throwing the plates?"
"I'd like to try juggling with plates."

"I always want to look at different things to my mum. But she's usually in too much of a hurry for us to stop."

"It can be a bit scary when there are crowds of people. Sometimes I think I might be lost, then I see Dad again."
"I got lost in the supermarket. They asked me my name, then they called my mum on the tannoy, so everybody could hear. Mum was cross, but I think <u>she</u> lost <u>me</u> really."

"If I got lost, I'd look for a policeman."
"What if you couldn't find one?"
"I'd ask a shopkeeper to help me."

"I hope I would get taken home in a police car, if I got lost."

"I was hiding in a doorway, and Mum thought I was lost. She was very angry, but it was only a joke."
"I expect your mum was worried."

"When we go out for the day, Dad always tells me and my brother where to go, like back to the car, if we lose him."

"My brother got lost when I was looking after him. I got really scared and it made me angry with him."
"My brother isn't allowed to look after me - Dad says he might not know what to do if I got hurt."

Have you ever been lost?
How did you feel?